ALEJAND...

PLUS 19 TOP HITS

Published by

WISE PUBLICATIONS
14-15 Berners Street, London W1T 3LJ, UK

Exclusive Distributors:

MUSIC SALES LIMITED
Distribution Centre, Newmarket Road,
Bury St Edmunds, Suffolk IP33 3YB, UK

MUSIC SALES PTY LIMITED
20 Resolution Drive,
Caringbah, NSW 2229, Australia

Order No. AM1002144
ISBN 978-1-84938-814-6
This book © Copyright 2010 Wise Publications,
a division of Music Sales Limited.

Edited by Jenni Wheeler.
Cover designed by Lizzie Barrand.

Printed in the EU

www.musicsales.com

ALEJANDRO

PLUS 19 TOP HITS

WISE PUBLICATIONS
PART OF THE MUSIC SALES GROUP
LONDON / NEW YORK / PARIS / SYDNEY / COPENHAGEN / BERLIN / MADRID / HONG KONG / TOKYO

Lady Gaga
Alejandro
Words & Music by Stefani Germanotta & RedOne

Spoken: I know that we are young, and I know that you may love me. But I just can't be with you like this anymore, Alejandro.

don't call my name,__ Ro - ber - to.__ A - le - jan - dro,__ A - le-jan - dro,__

A - le - a - le-jan - dro, A - le - a - le - jan - dro,__

A - le -jan - dro,__ A - le-jan - dro,__

1.

A - le - a - le-jan - dro, A - le - a - le-jan - dro.____

11

Alexandra Burke

All Night Long

Words & Music by Rico Love, James Scheffer,
Samuel Watters & Louis Biancaniello

1. I see ev'ry-bod-y a-round____ but it feels like we're in pri - vate.____ (Ooh.)____
(2.)-night the ad-mis-sion is free,____ now we're shut- tin' the club____ down..____ (Ooh.)____

15

Kylie

All The Lovers

Words & Music by Mima Stilwell & Jim Eliot

1. Dance, it's all I wan-na do.__ So won't you
2. Feel, can't you see there's so__ much here to

dance? I'm stand-ing here with you.__ Why won't you
feel? Deep in-side your heart__ you know I'm

move? I'll get in-side your groove 'cause I'm on
real. Can't you see that this is go-ing

21

fi - re, fi - re, fi - re, fi - re.

Pixie Lott

Boys And Girls

Words & Music by Phil Thornalley, Mads Hauge
& Victoria Lott.

Original key: D♭ major

Lively ♩ = 130

bright,   like I'm on the T. V.
good,   yeah,___ we're gon - na lose control.

My heart pumps as the bass drum___ thumps,___ you got - ta move when the
Turn it on,_____ make it___ strong,___ a good beat nev - er

floor - board jumps. Some - thing's go - ing on and I think it's go - ing on right now.___
hurt no one. Kick - ing up the dust and we're mak - ing ev - 'ry move___ we

Paloma Faith

Do You Want The Truth Or Something Beautiful?

Words & Music by Paloma Faith & Ed Harcourt

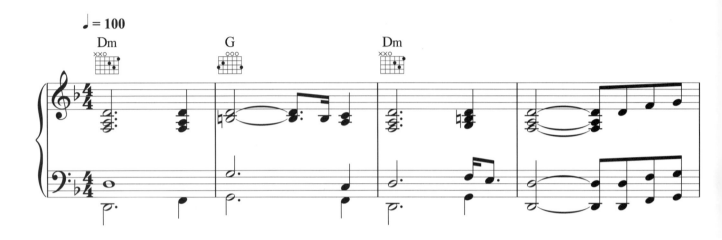

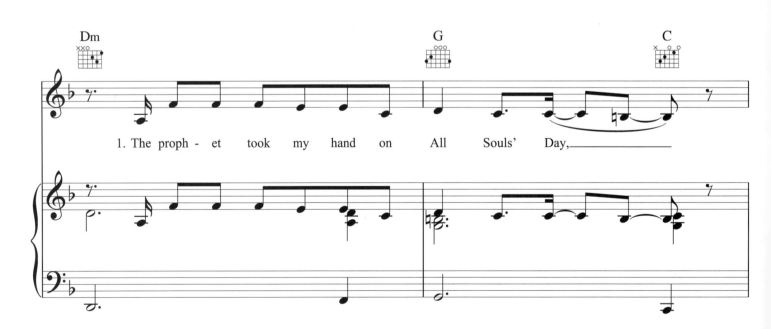

1. The proph - et took my hand on All Souls' Day,

truths a - side.____
hon-est truth____

To his ques - tions I re - plied.____
so I spit out lies that aimed to soothe.____

Do you want the truth or some-thing beau-ti-ful?_____

Just close your eyes_ and make be-lieve._

_____

Do you want the truth or some-thing beau-ti-ful?_____

1.

I am hap - py to de - ceive you.____

2.

I am hap - py to de -

39

Metric

Eclipse (All Yours)

Words by Emily Haines & James Shaw
Music by Emily Haines, James Shaw & Howard Shore

1. All the lives,

Kelis

4ᵗʰ Of July (Fireworks)

Words & Music by Kelis Rogers, Jean Baptiste, Damien Leroy, Jaime Munson,
Anthony Burns, Vanessa Fischer, Ronnie Morris & Jeff Scheven

Ellie Goulding

Guns And Horses

Words & Music by Ellie Goulding & John Fortis

61

Robyn
Hang With Me
Words & Music by Klas Ahlund

1. Will you tell__ me once a- -gain how we're gon - na be__ just friends?

If you're for real and not pre-tend, then I guess you can hang with me.__

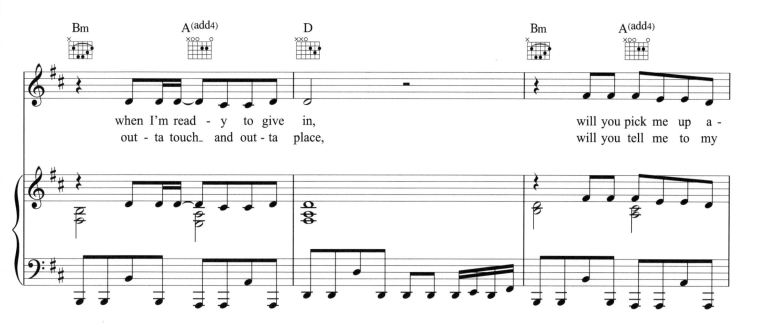

2. When my pa - tience, wear - ing thin,
3. When you see me drift a - stray,

when I'm read - y to give in, will you pick me up a -
out - ta touch__ and out - ta place, will you tell me to my

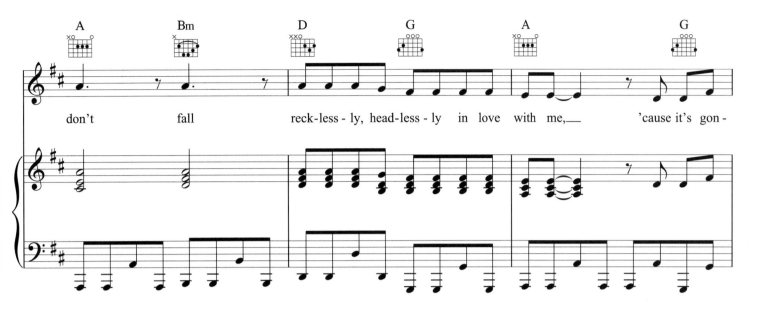

don't fall reck-less-ly, head-less-ly in love with me,___ 'cause it's gon-

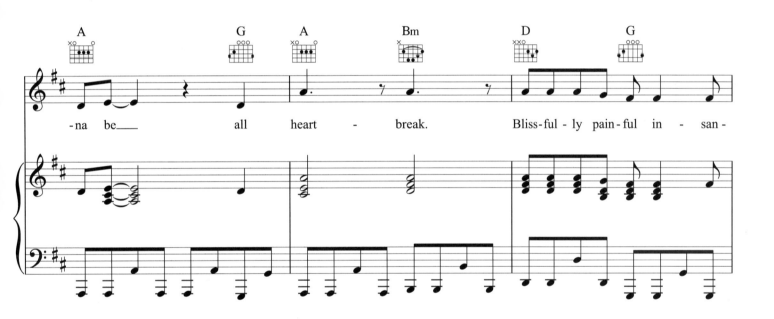

-na be___ all heart - break. Bliss-ful - ly pain-ful in - san-

To Coda ⊕

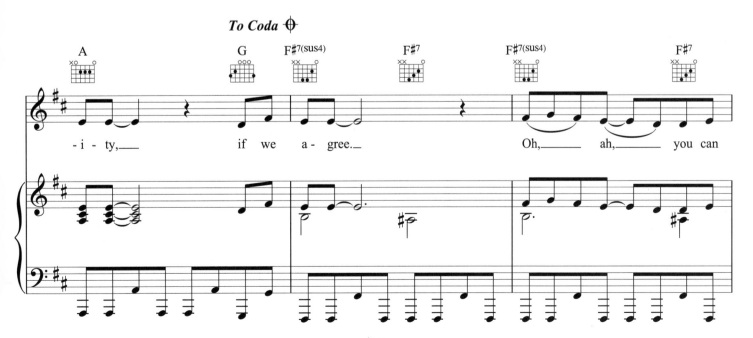

-i - ty,___ if we a - gree.___ Oh,_____ ah,___ you can

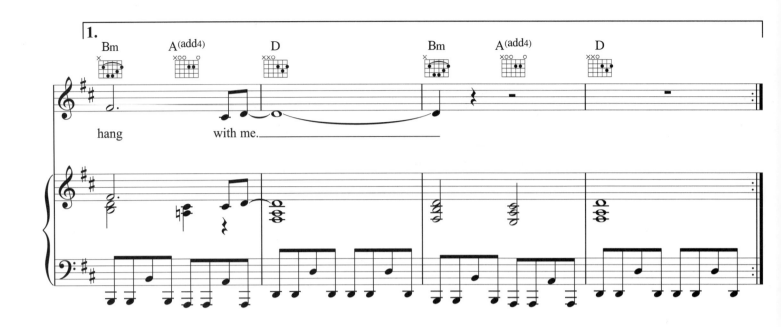

hang with me.

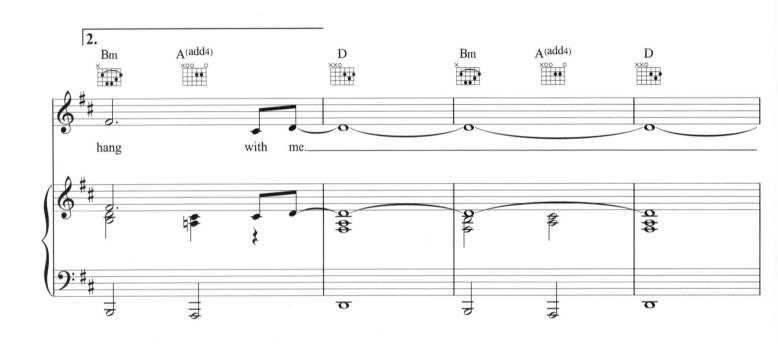

hang with me.

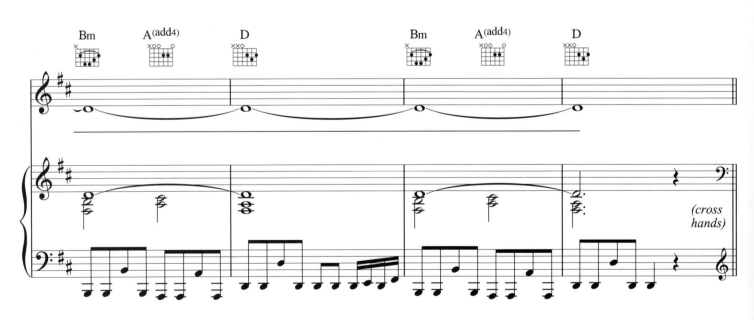

(cross hands)

N.C.

4. Will you tell___ me once a - gain

R.H.

L.H.

how we're gon - na be_____ just friends?

If you're for real and not pre - tend, then I guess you can

D.S. al Coda

hang with me.___

(cross back)

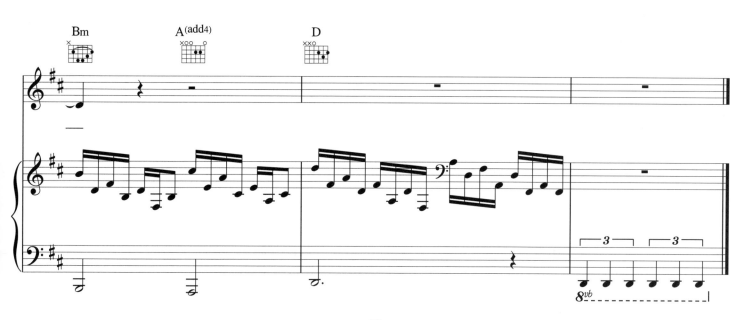

Diana Vickers

Once

Words & Music by Eg White & Cathy Dennis

Here we are, a careful distance.
Ashes burn the morning after.
Here's my heart, what's
Only know I'm

Touch them where it hurts,___ then___ you'll leave._____

D.S. al Coda

Coda

I'm on-ly gon-na let you kill me.___

Sky Ferreira

One

Words & Music by Christian Karlsson, Pontus Winnberg,
Sky Ferreira, Liv Bergman & Magnus Lidehall

Cheryl Cole

Parachute

Words & Music by Ingrid Michaelson & Marshall Altman

Rihanna

Rude Boy

Words & Music by Mikkel S. Eriksen, Tor Erik Hermansen, Esther Dean,
Makeba Riddick, Rob Swire & Robyn Fenty

Original key: G♯ major

♩ = 96

Eliza Doolittle
Skinny Genes
Words & Music by Eliza Caird, Matthew Prime & Tim Woodcock

1. I real - ly don't like your point___ of view. I
(2.) real - ly don't like your skin - ny jeans so

Slow

Rumer

Words & Music by Sarah Joyce

8vb throughout

You make me want to sing a - bout love ev - 'ry time I raise my head. You make me want to tell the whole world what I've found is good. Then they say slow,

Katy Perry

Teenage Dream

Words & Music by Katy Perry, Lukasz Gottwald, Max Martin,
Benjamin Levin & Bonnie McKee

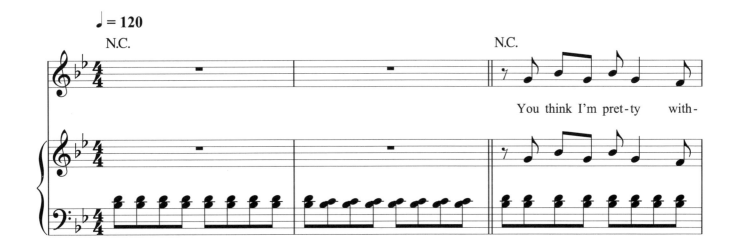

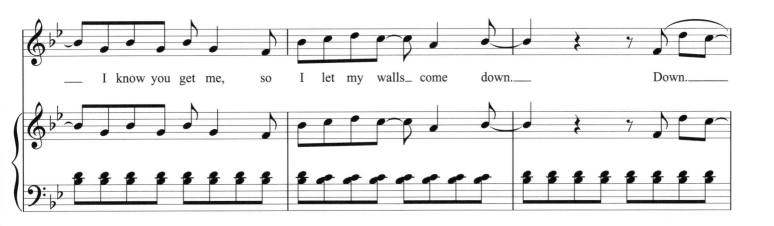

Alicia Keys

Try Sleeping With A Broken Heart

Words & Music by Jeff Bhasker, Alicia Keys
& Patrick Reynolds

bed,   lone - ly,   own me,   no - bod - y ev - er shut it down   like

you.   You wore the crown,   you made my bod - y feel heav - en bound.   Why don't you

hold me,   need me,   I thought you told me   you'd nev - er leave   me?

3. Look - in' in the sky   I could see your face,   and I know right where I   fit

D.S. al Coda

in.　　Take　me,　　　make　me,　　you know that al - ways be in

love　　with you,　　　right till＿ the＿ end.＿＿＿＿　Oh,＿＿ so to-night＿

Coda

An - y - bod - y　could　have　told＿＿　you　right　from　the　start,＿

＿ it's 'bout to fall　a - part.＿　　So rath - er than hold on　to　a bro - ken dream,＿

114

Beyoncé

Why Don't You Love Me

Words & Music by Angela Beyince, Beyoncé Knowles, Solange Knowles,
Jonathan Wells, Jesse Rankins & Eddie III Smith

Original key: A♭ minor

♩ = 138

(Spoken:) N-now, now, honey, you better sit down and look around, 'cause

you must have bumped your head. And I love you enough to talk some sense back into you, babe.

_ one to help me_ out;_____ you don't_ e - ven no - tice
-py with the nas-ty things I do._____ But you don't_ seem___ to be___ in

that.
tune.

Noth-in' not to love___ a-bout, noth-in' not to love a-bout_ me.

need__ a - bout__ me.___

May - be you're just not the one,__

or may - be you're just plain..._____

...dumb!

Florence + The Machine

You Got The Love

Words & Music by Anthony Stephens, John Bellamy,
Arnecia Harris & John Truelove

Original key: D♭ major

Ke$ha

Your Love Is My Drug

Words & Music by Pebe Sebert, Kesha Sebert
& Joshua Coleman

Original key: F♯ major

♩ = 120

1. May-be I need some re-hab, or may-be just need some sleep.
(2.) mum's tell-in' me I should think twice.

I got a sick ob-ses-sion, I'm see-in' it in my dreams.
But left to my own de-vi-ces, I'm ad-dict-ed; it's a cri-sis.

I'm look-in' down ev-'ry al-ley,
My friends think I've gone cra-zy,

123456789

Bringing you the words and the music

All the latest music in print... rock & pop plus jazz, blues, country, classical and the best in West End show scores.

- Books to match your favourite CDs.

- Book-and-CD titles with high quality backing tracks for you to play along to. Now you can play guitar or piano with yo favourite artist... or simply sing along!

- Audition songbooks with CD backing tracks for both male and female singers for all those with stars in their eyes.

- Can't read music? No problem, you can still play all the hits with our wide range chord songbooks.

- Check out our range of instrumental tutorial titles, taking you from novice to expert in no time at all!

- Musical show scores include *The Phanto Of The Opera*, *Les Misérables*, *Mamma Mia* and many more hit productions.

- DVD master classes featuring the techniques of top artists.